真美味！我们一起吃！
Yum! Let's Eat!

Thando Maclaren
Illustrated by Jacqueline East

Simplified Chinese translation by Sylvia Denham

Mantra Lingua

我是玛利亚，我的妈妈正在造菜汁捞面条。
真美味！我最喜欢吃！

I'm Maria and my mama's making pasta primavera.

Yum

Yum

Yummy!

My favourite!

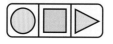

我的名字是格贝雅娜，我的家人喜欢吃香辣的辣椒和薄并。真美味！我最喜欢吃！

My name's Gabriela. My family loves eating hot, spicy chilli and fajitas.

Yum

Yum

Yummy!

My favourite!

我是卡力，我们去探访祖父时，
都会吃蒸丸子和焖辣羊肉。
真美味！我最喜欢吃！

I'm Khaled. We eat couscous and
lamb tagine when we visit Grandpa.

Yum
　　Yum
　　　　Yummy!

My favourite!

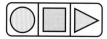

我是阿格达，我的祖母正在为我和姐姐造她拿手的波兰炖肉。真美味！我最喜欢吃！

My name's Agata. My granny is making her special bigos for me and my big sister.

Yum
    Yum
        Yummy!

My favourite!

我是杜恩，我喜欢吃青豆
米饭和羊肉咖喱。
真美味！我最喜欢吃！

I'm Dwayne and I love eating
rice and peas with goat curry.

Yum

Yum

Yummy!

My favourite!

我的名字是仪敏，我妈妈正在
造玉米炒鸡肉。
真美味！我最喜欢吃！

My name's Yi-Min. My mum is making
stir fry with chicken and baby corn.

Yum

　　　Yum

　　　　　　Yummy!

My favourite!

我是阿卑巴，我的家人喜欢吃
埃塞俄比亚薄饼和辛辣的烤炖肉。
真美味！我最喜欢吃！

I'm Abeba and my family loves
eating injera with spicy zigni.

Yum
　　Yum
　　　　Yummy!

My favourite!

我的名字是爱子，我正在跟
哥哥姐姐一起吃面条和寿司。
真美味！我最喜欢吃！

My name's Aiko. I'm eating
noodles and sushi with my
brother and sister.

Yum
　　Yum
　　　　Yummy!

　　　My favourite!

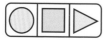

我是比蒂，我的祖母为爸爸
和我造焖扁豆、薄并及芒果
酸乳酪。
真美味！我最喜欢吃！

I'm Priti and my granny makes
dhal and roti, with mango lassi
for me and daddy.

Yum

  Yum

    Yummy!

My favourite!

我是查理，我正在与爸爸妈妈一起吃土豆碎肉馅饼。真美味！我最喜欢吃！

My name's Charlie. I'm having shepherd's pie with Mum and Dad.

Yum

Yum

Yummy!

My favourite!

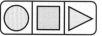

我是阿仙，我喜欢跟爸爸和
哥哥一起吃菜包及烤肉串。
真美味！我最喜欢吃！

I'm Yasin and I love eating
kebabs and dolma with Daddy
and my big brother.

Yum
    Yum
        Yummy!

My favourite!

Turkey

Poland

India

Mexico

Jamaica

Italy

Japan

Morocco

Ethiopia

UK

China